THE BIG BOX

AN ABC BOOK

WRITTEN BY JUDY NAYER
ART BY SUSAN SWAN

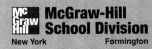

**McGraw-Hill
School Division**

New York   Farmington

1

"That is a big box!"
said Sam.

"What can we do with it?"
asked Miya.

"We can make an **alphabet** box," said Gina.

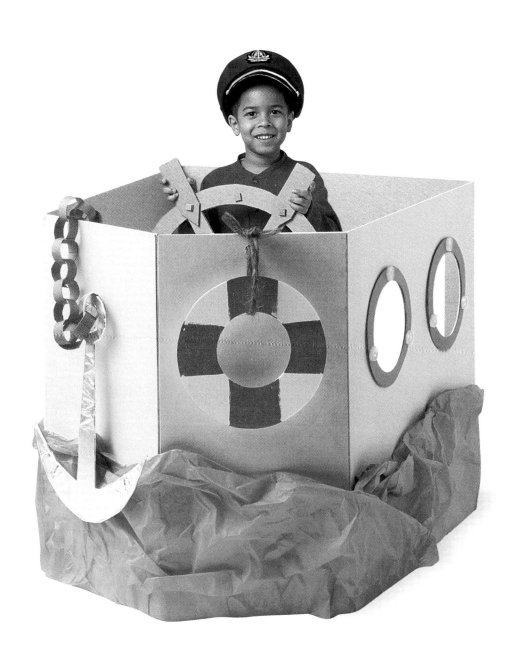

"We can make a **boat**,"
said Rob.

"We can make a **castle**,"
said Matt.

"We can make a **dinosaur**,"
said Miya.

"We can make an **elevator**,"
said Sam.

"We can make a **fire** truck,"
said Ann.

"We can make a **game**,"
said Rob.

"We can make a **house**,"
said Gina.

"We can make an **igloo**,"
said Matt.

"We can make a **jungle**,"
said Miya.

"We can make a **kitchen**,"
said Rob.

"We can make a **lake** and go swimming," said Gina.

"We can make a **mailbox**," said Miya.

"We can make a **nest**,"
said Sam.

"We can make an **octopus** with 8 arms," said Ann.

"We can make a **puppet** stage," said Rob.

"We can make a **quilt** for a bed,"
said Gina.

"We can make a **robot**,"
said Matt.

"We can make a **sandbox**," said Sam.

"We can make a **tunnel** and crawl through," said Miya.

"We can make a giant **umbrella**," said Rob.

"We can make a **van**,"
said Ann.

"We can make a **wagon**,"
said Sam.

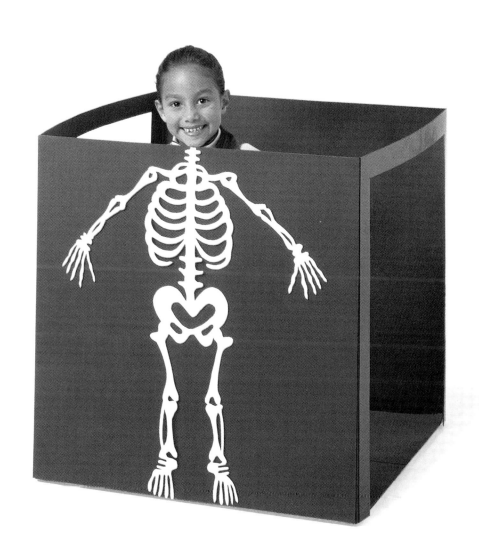

"We can make an **X-ray** machine," said Gina.

"We can paint **yellow** things
on the box," said Matt.

"We can make a **zebra** with black and white stripes," said Ann.

"So what will you make with the box?" asked Mom.

What would you make?